The Ambassador's Dog is a story of the magic of unexpected connections on a trail in Upper Mustang in Nepal. It is the tale of a small pup, with no name, and no family, who entrusted his dreams to the winds that swirled from the peaks of the high Himalaya and about the man to whom the winds carried the dreams and planted them silently in his heart.

Today, Lo Khyi lives in Haymarket, Virginia - far from his birthplace in Tsarang in Upper Mustang. He still has the spirit of an adventurer and still engages all he meets reminding them that dreams can come true and that there is courage and compassion and hope to be found in the world if our hearts are open to seeing them.

the ambassador's dog

Written by Scott H. DeLisi
Illustrated by Jane Lillian Vance

VAJRA
BOOKS

Published and Distributed 2020 by
Vajra Books
Jyatha, Thamel, P.O. Box 21779, Kathmandu, Nepal
Tel.: 977-1-4220562, 4246536
e-mail: vajrabooksktm@gmail.com
www.vajrabooks.com.np

ISBN 978-9937-733-22-9

Layout by Nabindra Dongol
Printed and Bound at Archana, www.archanapress.com

To Sofie, Leo and Luca, and Vivian and Arthur:
May you always remember that puppies really *can* speak;
you just have to know how to listen.

༄༅། །ལས་སྨོན་བརྟེན་འབྲེལ་འཛོམས་པས་ཨེ་ཤེ་ཀོ་ཏེ་ཏེ་ལེ་སེས་
མཚོག་སྐུ་ལ་ཐུང་དུ་བརྒོད་ཟང་ལ་བསྐྱོད་སྐུབས་ཏེ་མ་ལའེ་དེ་གའ་ཁྱུ་
ཁྱི་བཟང་བོ་ཞིག་ཁོ་ཀི་འཕུད་པས་ཁོ་པི་གིན་ཐུ་དག་འན་དང་འཛེ་
བའི་ཤོག་ཕྱག་དུ་ཆུ་བན་ནི་ཏ་དུང་གནས་མས་ཤུ་རྒྱུན་ལ་རེ་སྐྱོས་
པས་ཁོ་རི་སྐྱུ་ཕྱུག་སྤྱར་བ་ཞིང་བྱམས་པས་གསོ་སྐྱོང་
གནང་ཞིང་ཉི་འི་གོ་ཏེ་བ་ནོ་གཞིན་སྤྱོད་ ཕུག་ རྐྱམས་ལ་སྐྱོན་
གཉེ་ཏུ་འདེ་དག་རྐྱམས་ཉེ་གང་ནེ་ཏེ་ཞེ་མེ་ཀོ་ཏུ་ལེ་
ལེས་མཚོག་དང་སྐྱུ་ཏུ་ཏུ་བེ་བལ་ལ་རེ་སྤྱོན་ ཕུག་ དང་འི་
འདི་འཕྲེལ་བ་ཨེན་ཚོ་ར་མ་ལུས་འཕུལ་ཀི་ར་སྐྱོ་འགྲོ་བ་ཏ་
དཔས་འཕྲི་རེ་བས་ཁེ་མ་ཏུ་མཚོ་མས་པ་རྒ་དྲུན་པས་སྐྱོ་ལོ་
2020.2.28 ཨོ་རི་ནི་ཨེ་ལེ་ཀོ་ཏེ་ མཚོག་དཀ་ཏི་མཚོག་སྐྱོན་འཕུག་ས་དང་
བཅས་བཞི་བདེ་དཔལ་ལ་སྐྱོད་པའི་རྒུ་འཕྲུར་ཐེ།

Scott H. DeLisi and Jane Lillian Vance are grateful to receive Mustang's Amchi Tsampa Ngawang Lama's blessing of our book about Lo Khyi and the karmic interconnection between the Ambassador and his dog. With this prayer from his heart and his hand, Tsampa also commends Ambassador DeLisi's loving compassion, and the resulting deepened connection between Nepal and America, blessing all of our readers.

I know all really good stories begin,
"Once upon a time...." But can you still
begin a story that way if it is true?
Because this story is. Just ask Lo Khyi.
He will tell you his tale.

You just have to know how to listen.

Or ask the man who met Lo Khyi one
day, and whose life was never the same.

This story begins before Lo Khyi had a name. He was tiny. So tiny. He couldn't say for sure how many days it had been since his life began. There was the warmth of his mother. That, he remembered. And his brothers and sisters. They didn't have names yet either, but he knew them by their smell and the way they pushed and squirmed together as they sought their mother's milk. He remembered them, too.

But then, suddenly, there was nothing more he could remember of his mother and brothers and sisters.

Although the puppy was too tiny to see yet, too tiny to hear yet, he knew only that he was alone. Totally alone.

It was cold without the warmth of his mother and brothers and sisters. He didn't know where they were or how they had become lost to him. He only knew he was alone in this place where the wind blew down from the mountain peaks and chilled his tiny body, covered only by the finest coat of soft puppy hair.

If this small pup could have read a map, he would
have learned he was in the village of Tsarang,
high in the mountains, on the Tibetan Plateau, in
a country called Nepal. If he could have read a
calendar, he would have known it was the end of
February—wintertime in the mountains.

But the pup with no name, and now with no family,
could not read a map or a calendar. He only knew
it was cold. He was alone. And he was hungry.

But he wasn't scared. I don't know how that little
puppy could be so brave. I don't think I would have
been. But he was. The puppy was determined to live.

One day passed. Then another. The puppy lay on the edge of a trail. He was shivering very hard now. He was so cold and so weak he could barely move, and he was oh so hungry. But then, something happened.

Do you remember that special feeling when you were little? When your Mom or Dad, or Nana or Papa, would reach for you, their hands, strong and warm, gently folding around you as they swept you into their arms? Snuggling you. So comfortable. So safe.

Well, that is what happened to the puppy that cold February day in the village of Tsarang.

A boy, perhaps 15 or 16 years old, with dark hair and with brown eyes that missed nothing in the world around him, was walking along the path. He saw the very small puppy lying alone, his tiny head and floppy ears resting on his front paws.

The forlorn pup looked so cold, so miserable, that Karchung (for that was the boy's name) knelt down beside the pup.

"Little brother," he said, "this will not do."

He reached out with his strong, warm hands and he scooped the pup with no name into his arms,

unzipped the heavy fleece that he wore, and tucked the puppy inside against the warm wool shirt underneath.

Zipping his fleece against the morning winds that caused the prayer flags on the small shrine nearby to dance and sway, he settled the puppy against his chest and set off towards his home in the nearby village of Saukre.

11

They say that those winds that blow across the Tibetan Plateau carry the hopes and wishes that are written on the prayer flags, onward to the heavens. I don't know if that is true, but I like to think it is. So did the little puppy, who hoped that his truest dreams might be carried on those winds. He had not inscribed them on a flag but he hoped that the winds would carry his dream nonetheless.

It might surprise you that a puppy so young could have a dream, but he did. He might have been tiny, but this puppy knew deep in his heart that he would somehow find a home. And he knew, with a certainty that came from deep within his being, that the borders of his world would extend even farther than a Himalayan Golden Eagle could see from its lofty mountain aerie.

The pup did not really know that a bigger world lay beyond the Tibetan Plateau that was his home — he was, after all, just a tiny puppy. But something told him his destiny lay beyond the mountains of the plateau and it made him long for the future to come.

This dream might have seemed too big for such a little pup to dream but, fortunately, our dreams are not measured by the size of our bodies but by the size of our hearts. And when the winds start to blow, as they did that day, it is okay to allow the hopes in our hearts to grow wings. And that is what the puppy did.

"Please winds," the puppy thought sleepily, as he burrowed into the warmth of Karchung's body, "please carry my dreams. Please let them come true."

That is what the puppy asked the winds. And the winds heard the pup's wish, and they carried his hopes and dreams down the mountains, through the forests, and over the rivers that flowed across the land. The winds carried the puppy's dreams to Kathmandu, the biggest city in Nepal. They carried his dreams to a man who felt the breeze brush his face and stir his soul with an unexpected longing. And at that moment, a small puppy's dream silently took root in his heart.

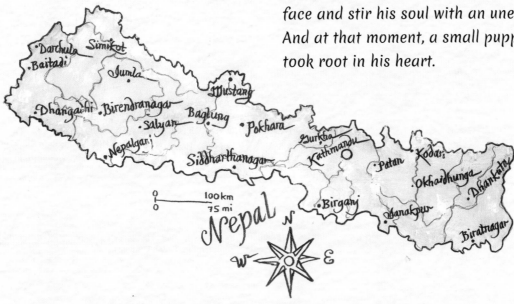

The puppy snuggled contentedly against Karchung.
He even slept a bit. Karchung's strides were steady
and smooth. He seemed to flow across the hillsides
and the rough trail. The rocks and ridges had been
Karchung's playground since he was a little boy
and he knew them as well as you know the way to
your favorite ice cream shop.

In no time at all, Karchung came to his village. He
unzipped his fleece and the puppy shook himself
awake.

Karchung set the pup down in a small shed that
blocked the chill wind. It felt so good to be warm
and to lay on a mound of straw that smelled of
sunshine and earth and of all the animals that lived

in the shed. It felt so good, that the puppy almost forgot how hungry he was. But only "almost."

And then, the puppy smelled a most glorious smell.

It was tsampa, although the puppy - who had never tasted anything but his mother's milk - did not know it by that name. Karchung had placed a small bowl of the porridge, made from roasted barley and mixed with butter tea and goat's milk, in front of the puppy.

The pup ate and ate and ate. He licked the last drops from his whiskers and then, overwhelmed by how his life had changed in just a few short hours, the puppy put his head down on his paws and did one of the things that puppies do best. He slept.

When the puppy awoke, something else had changed. Light and shadow were transforming into shapes filled with color and substance. And the noises he heard were not just a jumble of sound, but instead, each began to tell a story of life in the village.

He marveled as the world came alive around him and it seemed that every minute his eyes became sharper and his hearing better. And, after eating another bowl of that most delicious tsampa, he was also getting stronger. His wobbly legs became firm and he wanted to play and jump and run.

If you had met this puppy you would have laughed to see the huge heavy paws on which he pranced. Paws that seemed made for a far bigger dog. But the people knew this little puppy would one day grow to be a very big dog indeed. You see, this small ball of energy racing along the paths that crisscrossed the village, was one of the great Tibetan mastiffs, like those that guarded the palace of the King of Mustang.

Those dogs were black and brown, with white accents adorning their coats. With big heavy heads and broad chests, they roamed the palace walls at night like restless lions, daring anyone to cross into their king's domain. Their voices were deep and echoed back from the slopes of the hills when they called out their challenges. They were the bhote kukur - the dogs of the mountains. They were the big dogs, from which the other big dogs we know today are descended. And the pup was one of them. He was a bhote kukur - a mountain dog from the Kingdom of Mustang, which was once known as the Kingdom of Lo.

This pup was different from most of his kind, however. His blue-grey coat was the color of the land itself - as if that dust of the plateau, carried constantly on the wind, had become a part of his being, to travel with him wherever his dreams might lead.

He had a large white blaze on his chest that stood in vivid contrast to his dusky coat, and he was distinguished further by the chestnut brown stripes above his eyes; stripes that the people of the village claimed were the mark of "four eyes" - a mystical, magical mark, that foretold wisdom.

And the eyes that lay beneath those chestnut brows were wide, slightly almond shaped, and a mesmerizingly brilliant blue. A blue that demanded your attention like the cobalt blue skies of Mustang that dramatically frame the snowy mountain peaks on a clear day. A striking, amazing, and powerful blue, that told you immediately that - just as he had dreamed - this pup was indeed like no other.

I can't tell you what secret ingredient Karchung's mother, who was called Dawa, put in the tsampa that the puppy ate, but each day he grew bigger and his coat not only grew thicker but you would marvel at its incredible softness, that is, if the puppy stayed still long enough for you to pet him.

The puppy, you see, was always in motion. When he wasn't chasing the chickens and prancing around the goats he was restlessly roaming the village, exploring every corner of Saukre.

The people of the village recognized that this handsome blue-gray puppy had a wandering spirit. And, although the people were kind, the puppy sensed that none of them were the family of which he had dreamed. And so he waited. And every day he gazed down the trail that led back to Tsarang and then to a world beyond the plateau.

Karchung had never been beyond the village of Tsarang. Neither had his parents. Nor had most of the people of the village. They were content with their lives in the mountains.

The chickens, the goats, and the donkeys the pup met had never left the mountains either. They had no desire to do so. They too were content with their lives high on the plateau and with their homes in Saukre.

But the puppy - the bhote kukur born in the heart of those mountains - knew that his future lay down the trail and beyond. And so, he waited. He knew his dreams would find him and he would find his dreams.

The puppy waited quietly. He waited with dignity.
Calmly. Sure that his future lay down the path he
watched so intently every day.

The people of Saukre worried that the restless
spirit in the puppy would lead him to follow some
call only he heard and take him far away from
them.

So they used a khata, a ceremonial silk blessing
scarf, to tie the puppy to a metal rod pounded into
the ground on the edge of the trail. But the pup did
not mind. He sat. He waited. He watched.

The days passed. Then, one morning, when the pup
awoke, the air around him was alive with energy.
Karchung did not feel it. The chickens scratching in
the dirt did not feel it. The goats wandering through
the lanes did not feel it. But the puppy felt it, and
his heart raced.

He gobbled down his tsampa and then went out into the day. The worst of the winter chills were gone but a fog still shrouded Saukre early that April morning. The blue-gray pup was almost invisible, blending into the drifting wisps of mist as he raced for his perch overlooking the trail. Karchung knew where the pup was bound and followed along behind. As he had every day for the past week, he tied the pup to the metal rod. The pup did not mind. He sat on his rock, looked down the trail, and waited.

The sun rose higher and the mists gave way to a blue sky that matched the puppy's eyes. The village had come alive as the morning passed. Everyone was in motion. Except the pup. He still waited.

At ten o'clock, people in the village stopped for tea. But the pup waited. Every nerve was tingling. He sat so straight. So strong. So handsome. And he waited.

Suddenly, the pup sat even straighter, if such a thing was possible. There. In the distance. People were moving. They came closer and closer and closer. In front was a man. A man in a white shirt and wearing a blue cap.

His white beard spoke of the passage of years, but the fact that he hiked in these high mountain passes told the pup that his spirit was strong. The man's eyes were kind and his voice gentle. The puppy knew that this was his man. This was why he had waited. He knew it, even if the man did not.

The pup mustered all the dignity that a five-week old puppy could muster. He sat still. But his heart raced. He met the man's eyes and held them and, for the first time, the puppy spoke.

The man's name was Scott. He was the man to whom the wind carrying the puppy's dream had whispered weeks before in Kathmandu. By the time that wild wind blowing off the mountains had reached him it had diminished to only a gentle breeze, but it still had the strength to plant the seed of that puppy's vision deeply in Scott's heart. He did not know that the seed was there. He did not nurture it or encourage its growth, but slowly it blossomed inside him,

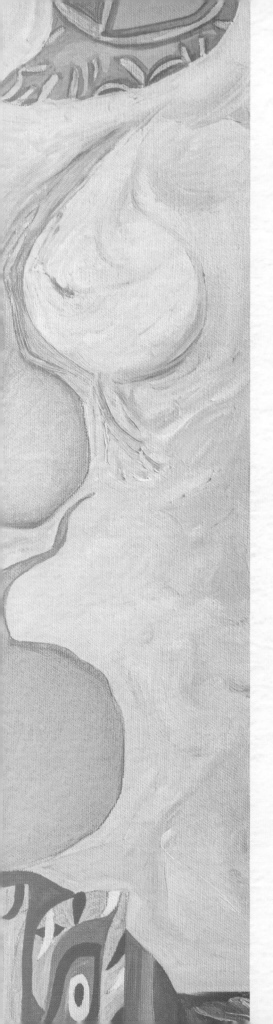

singing softly, waiting until the time was right to be revealed.

Scott and his companions were bound for the fabled walled city of Lo Manthang. One of those ancient places at the top of the world that wanderers are called to explore. They still had far to go, but as they set off that morning, after spending a night in Tsarang, their destination that day was the Lo Gekar Monastery, nestled above the village of Saukre.

The trail they followed, as you may have guessed, was the trail where the puppy waited and watched. And, when they came to Saukre, Scott paused. There, before him, was a puppy. An amazing puppy.

It was the eyes that drew Scott's gaze. It is why

23

he saw the pup despite his blue-grey camouflage that allowed him to blend into the rocky hillside. Those blue eyes blazed in the morning light. They met Scott's eyes. And at that moment, the puppy's dream, the dream that had taken root inside Scott's heart weeks before, began to stir.

Then, their eyes met, and, for the first time, the puppy spoke.

"Wait a minute," you cry! "Puppies can't talk!"

I understand why you say that. I always thought that puppies only spoke in fairy tales. Not in true stories. And I did tell you that the story is true.

And it is.

But the puppy did speak that day.

Just ask Scott.

He told me that on that April morning - and many times since - he heard that puppy's words as clearly as you hear your mom or dad when they call you to tell you to take a bath or to come to dinner. I believe him. You should too.

Perhaps the puppy's dream that had settled in Scott's heart let the puppy's words reach his ears. Or maybe it was because Scott knew how to listen with his heart and not just his ears. I really don't know. I only know that the puppy spoke, that Scott heard him, and that day, the world changed for them both.

The puppy's blue eyes met Scott's hazel ones. And, for the first time, the puppy spoke.

Looking at Scott, the puppy greeted him.

"Dhai," he said, which means older brother in Nepali, "come here."

Scott set his pack on the ground. He didn't think it strange that the puppy had spoken to him. And it was only polite, he thought, to return the greeting of this puppy that had called him "older brother" and that had invited him to share his rocky perch.

Climbing up to the rock on which the puppy sat, Scott lowered himself to the ground next to this handsome blue-eyed pup. The puppy jumped onto Scott's lap. He greeted Scott as pups do, first licking his hands and then putting his paws up on Scott's shoulders.

His raspy pink tongue licked Scott on both cheeks and then the puppy looked up into Scott's eyes and calmly informed him, "Dhai, you do not know this, but I am your dog."

"Really?" Scott asked.

"Really!" the pup replied.

Scott considered this for a moment and then, looking again at the pup's earnest face and deep blue eyes, said, "You may be right."

"I am," the puppy confidently assured Scott.

Scott studied the pup nestled in his lap. He was pretty certain that none of his companions had heard the conversation with the puppy.

One of them even came over to Scott and respectfully said, "Sir, we need to continue."

Scott, you see, was a diplomat, and not only a

diplomat but an Ambassador. The American Ambassador to Nepal, to be even more precise. That meant that some people thought that Scott was an important man, and in many ways he might have been. But not because people called him "Your Excellency," and not because he was usually driven around in a big car and was in charge of a lot of things.

If you asked Scott, he would tell you he didn't care about having a fancy title or a big car or being important. He cared about helping people in Nepal. He cared about building friendships and about helping the people of Nepal to be safer and stronger. These were the sorts of things that Scott cared about. And, because the people of America cared about these things too, Scott was proud to serve them as a diplomat.

Scott had learned that sometimes people just need a helping hand from someone who cares. And, as an ambassador, Scott had lots of chances to show people that America cared. He had the chance to help people who were poor to build a better life for their families. He had a chance to help people who were sick to get care from doctors and nurses. Most of all, he had the chance to work together with the people of Nepal to build a future of hope in a world that can always use more hope for brighter futures.

The people who were traveling with Ambassador Scott helped him in that work. But on that sunny morning they were thinking mostly about the ambassador's schedule, not about this little pup waiting along the trail. They knew that there was work to do that day and that they needed to visit the monastery and to see other places in Mustang where America could help. They had many miles yet to hike.

So they said to Scott, "Sir, we should go on."

Scott got up, and set the puppy down. He thanked him for the conversation and told the pup he needed to climb the hill and visit the Monastery. The pup didn't worry.

He just said, "Dhai, don't forget. I am your dog."

Scott went up the hill. He visited the monastery. Then he sat outside, with his back against a wall of the ancient building, and gazed out over the hillside as he ate the lunch they had packed that morning. His thoughts returned to the puppy. He thought about his blue eyes. He thought about his dusty colored coat. He thought about his raspy tongue, his big heavy paws, his trusting gaze. And he thought about the puppy's last words to him. "Dhai, don't forget. I am your dog."

Scott stood up. He strapped on his pack. It was time to go. Back down the hill. Down to Saukre and then onward as they continued their journey to Lo Manthang.

Down the hill Scott went. Walking quickly. Faster. Down the hill towards Saukre where the puppy sat waiting.

When he got to Saukre, Karchung's uncle, Wangdi Rapkay - one of the village elders - asked Scott and his team to come and have tea. Scott thanked him, but asked first if someone could tell him about the puppy who, as you might have guessed, was still waiting there along the trail.

Wangdi explained to Ambassador Scott how Karchung had found the puppy a few weeks before, weak and all alone. He told Ambassador Scott how the puppy had thrived eating tsampa and living in the village, but that the little dog seemed to have the heart of a wanderer.

And then Scott asked a question that caused the puppy to almost leap for joy.

He asked, "Please, tell me, is this puppy for sale?"

The people of the village looked at Ambassador Scott.

Wangdi gently said, "Excellency, here in Tibet, the word for dog is 'khyi' which is also the

word for happiness. So, we consider dogs to be the source of happiness. That means we do not sell them, we give them as gifts."

Scott's heart was touched deeply by these words, and the puppy's dream that had been planted in his heart weeks before by the wind that had originated here on the plateau, came fully to life. Its song thrummed in his blood.

And Scott was not the only one to feel the energy of that dream. The puppy also felt his dream, the dream that he had entrusted to the winds, come to life in Scott. Here was his person. Here was the man who would help the puppy find the home and the family he had dreamed of. This was the moment.

Scott told me later that he could not explain how he knew that this puppy was meant to be part of his life. He just did. He did not think. He did not ask whether it made sense.

He just turned to Karchung's uncle and said, "The idea of dogs being the source of happiness is wonderful and I understand why you would not sell them, but give them instead as gifts. But tell me," he continued, "is it appropriate to give a gift in return?"

"That would be very nice," Wangdi agreed with a smile.

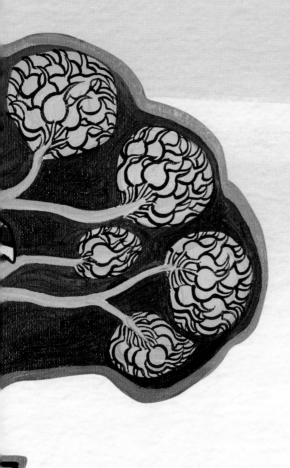

31

"Is the gift of rupees [which is the money they use in Nepal] a good gift?" Scott asked.

"Indeed!" said Wangdi.

Scott looked at the pup. The pup looked at Scott. And Scott reached into his pocket and pulled out all the rupees he could find and he offered them to Karchung. Karchung beamed. The rupees would help his family so much. He was thrilled. And then he untied the pup from the metal rod and the puppy jumped into Scott's arms.

The two of them walked together to Wangdi's home where they sat around a wooden table to have a cup of hot tea and to talk. But even though Ambassador Scott talked of many things with Wangdi and others in the village, he spoke as well with the pup.

The puppy, resting in the Ambassador's arms looked up at him serenely content.

"I told you I was your dog, Dhai," he whispered sleepily.

"You did indeed," Scott replied. "And you were right."

"I know," was the last thing the puppy said before he dozed off.

The puppy's trek with Scott through the land of his birth was a journey of discovery. Each day brought new experiences that opened the puppy's eyes to a world that was much bigger than the villages of Tsarang or Saukre. But no surprise might have been greater than what happened the first night that Scott and the pup spent together on the trail.

When they reached the teahouse where they would stop that night, the pup stared. He had never been inside a place where people actually lived, and everything was new and strange. But, as I told you, this pup was very brave and with Scott by his side he was even braver.

He played under the table at which Scott and his friends sat. He gnawed on the willow sticks Scott had tied together to make him his first chew toy, and he lapped up the milk and porridge Scott gave him until his tummy was as so full he could barely move.

When night fell, Scott took the puppy outside and much to the pup's surprise and delight, Scott stayed by his side while they explored the barnyard together.

Scott laughed when the pup snuck up on the chickens and launched surprise attacks that filled the barnyard with indignant squawks.

And Scott smiled to see the pup jump with excitement when snowflakes began to fall, coating the ground and the pup with white down.

When the pup tired from his explorations and play, he began to look about to see if there was a shed which could protect him from the snow and the winds.

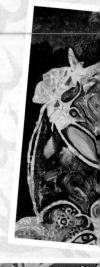

But before he could give further thought to where he would sleep that night, Scott swooped him into his arms and carried him back to the room in the teahouse where Scott had laid his sleeping bag on a wooden platform covered with a thin mat.

As Scott crawled into his sleeping bag he lifted the puppy, who smelled of earth and hay and the barnyard in which he had always slept, onto the platform with him.

The room may have been bare and chilly, and the platform hard and rough, but to the pup it was the grandest thing he had ever experienced. He curled up on the silky soft sleeping bag. He pressed against Scott's warmth and nestled his head on Scott's shoulder. Scott's arm enfolded him. It was perfect.

As they lay there waiting for sleep to come, Scott looked at the sleepy blue-eyed pup thoughtfully.

"You know," Scott told him, "everyone we meet will want to hear your story. They will want to know about the little pup from Mustang who waited on a trail, trusting in his dreams. They will want to hear how you had the courage to go on, believing that your dreams, carried by the wild winds, would bring me to you. It is, I think, a good story. One that people should hear."

And listening to these words, the little pup's heart swelled with pride and love and joy.

"Maybe," Scott continued, "you'd like to be a diplomat too. Helping people. Your story can remind those we meet that it is good to dream and to believe, and that our dreams can come true. And they will see us together and know, that when we work as partners, anything is possible. I think," Scott added with a laugh, "you could be a very fine DiploDog."

The pup liked the sound of that. He snuggled closer and sighed contentedly. Then Scott spoke again.

"One more thing, little brother. If we are going to stay together and you become a DiploDog you will need a name."

From the road, you
look up.
From the Himalayas,
no one looks down.
Their oldest pines fall
into place
Like hairs in a long
dark braid.

Braiding amulets into
their hair,
Or precious corals, or
old turquoises,
Old Tibetan women
carry the mountains
Piecemeal, as stony
haloes.

A grandmother and a
grandfather,
Like two sheep's-eye
agates;
Their grandchild
between them
Like the third eye
growing.

A Tibetan refugee
under the well
Turns her wrist
veins up.
The doctor's fing
hear her stori
The pulse of a
pursued by wo

Long white calla lilies,
and rhododendron
ed as cherry snowcones;
onkeys grow as brown
as earth
d groom the patient
ground.

n wishes move
e curtains
rge prayers
ter as small flags.
ky wall-papers
ints frequent
ens.

Old grandmothers' bedrooms
are wall-papered
With clumps of bamboo,
and leopards grasping
These Himachal hills
and
Curtains of forest.

Tractors go down to
the brooks
To bathe like sunny
elephants.
Their owners take
nettles and
Scrub their tired
wheels.

Himachal bubbles with
cherries,
Apples, boulders, donkeys,
plums;
And clouds relax and
curl
Like barnyard cats and
dragons.

A pilgrim on her way up
stops
To look at a refugee's
outdoor store.
The table is a
roadside stone
With a mirage of
merchandise.

The nun sucks a
tangerine,
The monk bites
burgundy a
The sparrow s
cauliflowe
The mountain
crunches t

And it was true. He did.

Scott thought of the land that they were traveling in and its ancient history as the Kingdom of Lo. And he thought of the people of Saukre who had told him that the word "khyi" meant both "dog" and "happiness" in Tibetan.

So, as they lay together and Scott stroked the pup's head and scratched him gently behind his ears, Scott offered an idea.

"If you agree," Scott told the pup, "I would like to call you 'Lo Khyi' because you are not only a dog from Lo but you are also, for me, the happiness of Lo and you always will be."

The pup pondered this thing. This name that his man offered him. He had not worried about having a name before this but men, it seemed, longed to give names to the things they loved, as if in doing so they see them more clearly.

And the pup knew that this was a gift from Scott. A gift not only of a name, but also of love. And that thought settled over him like a cloak and warmed him even more than Scott's arm around him that drew them close together.

"Lo Khyi" he decided, would be a fine name indeed. "Lo Khyi, the DiploDog."

He sighed with contentment and, with that, both he and Scott fell asleep.

In the morning, the sun reflected brightly off the snow that had settled lightly on the ground the night before. The air was still sharp with cold but there was a hint of warmth in the breeze that foretold that the snow would soon disappear as the group continued their journey that would soon lead them far from Lo Khyi's home. But that did not scare the pup. He knew it was meant to be.

Once, he had been a small pup with no name, but now he was Lo Khyi - the dog whose dreams were carried by the wind. Now he was Lo Khyi, the DiploDog - whose story would touch the lives of all that he met.

His tail curled proudly over his back. His blue eyes flashed and sparkled with excitement. Lo Khyi was descending from the mountains and together with Scott he would see the world.